Stronger Faster Shorter

Flash Fictions

David Swann

Flash: The International Short-Short Story Press

First published 2015
by Flash: The International Short-Short Story Press
c/o Department of English, University of Chester
Parkgate Road, Chester CH1 4BJ, UK

Edited by Peter Blair and Ashley Chantler

Cover designed by
LIS Graphics Team, University of Chester

Printed and bound in the UK by
LIS Print Unit, University of Chester

ISBN 978-0-9931822-0-4

Contents

Tracks

The cricket team's scorer wore grey shorts and had lovely white knees. Dogs surprised him, cats were daft. His ears were delicate and small, and the light shone through their workings. Sometimes I found him staring at the ground, watching the little things that live under our feet.

But that was before the illness weakened his grip on the pencil that recorded those five-bar gates which proved him a priest in cricket's mystery.

Afterwards, on many of the days we called, his parents pointed to the upstairs window, where they'd carefully drawn the curtains. Paul couldn't come out, they told us. He was badly again.

Years later, when I learned that 'mystery' means *the closing of the mouth*, I remembered the freckles dotted like scoring-marks across his face. I thought of his thin grey lips and the joys they briefly knew.

He lived in Little Belfast, an Irish estate under a Lancashire hill. We bent coins on the tracks that split our worlds.

He contained some sweetness the cancer never killed, a happiness with his own legs and feet – a child who sometimes stopped dead and stared at things.

The clouds, lads. Look at the clouds.

Then we'd follow his finger to the sky, and tell him what we thought.

It looks like a whale.

Does it heckalike, it looks like a cloud!

Paul shrugged and ran on again, deeper into the day. His pockets jangled as he squeezed through the fence by the railway.

Sometimes I glance up from my books and remember him there on the embankment, the breath wheezing in his chest. I think of our coin perched, ready – and him studying it, thrilled by our plan, thrilled by the glare.

And I hear it rushing again towards us, this force that none of us could tame or stop. This thing that sent us tumbling into the bracken, that trembled through the coin and the rail.

Running the Yards

Lancashire, 1975

And we'll climb the walls into the neighbours' yards, like Frazz said. Nowt else to do, might as well. Running the Yards. Down one wall, up the other. One yard at a time. The whole block in four minutes …

'Thirty houses?' groans Bodey.

Frazz nods.

And we'll sken in their bathrooms. Look for tits and fannies.

'Puff!' he calls Bodey.

Bodey's the first onto Ma Baker's wall, his hands searching out cracks.

Woooooh. We beat through the old bag's washing, a load of white ghosts. Frazz puts soot on her sheets. Bodey stops to sniff her knickers, all showy now, wanting Frazz to be watching.

But only Ma Baker's cat is interested.

No time. We stampede Number 60. Easy. But Number 62 are sunbathing round the back.

'Shine a light!' goes the bloke.

They shake their sickly fists, but you can do what you like, they're all on kidney machines.

Houses pass in a blur. 64, 66, 68. Women look up

from chip-pans, fellas from their porn. I concentrate on breathing; too much laughing and climbing.

Bodey's half-dead when we reach the crucial one. Number 74. He keeps looking behind him.

Frazz takes the Train Robbers' wall like a horse. It's that elephant spunk he's been guzzling. Muscle-building powder, specially mixed for weightlifters.

We land in the yard, demented, gasping. And there's the wife staring out, spiking her beehive.

'Train Robbers!' Frazz warns in a rasp.

'Ronnie!' she shouts, right hoity-toity. 'Ronnie!'

Frazz stares at her, confident. We have our suspicions about the Train Robbers. No jobs, tons of dosh.

Ronnie, like that's his name, wanders out in a vest, acting casual, as if he never robbed a train in his life. We stand under their wall, breathing. The wall looks like it was built to keep out Picts.

'Will you just stand there?' she asks her husband. 'They called you a Train Robber!'

He tosses his cigarette into the drain and steps across the yard, scratching hair on his chest. It's his vest. I'm frightened of his vest.

'Want to see what I done with that guard?' he growls.

And his shadow's too big to climb out from.

The People in the Desert

Our neighbour had perfected his silence. In the evenings, he'd stand on the front doorstep and stare into space, breathing smoke into the street.

Mum said to leave him in peace, so I'd lump a ball around while secretly watching him, trying to learn his craft. Silence was my ambition, I think. Maybe it still is.

There was nothing frightening about him, no fence around his silence; you could go in it if you wanted to. On days when I was brave, I'd ask him about his car, his brand of cigarettes, our neighbours. That was the only way I found to enter his silence – by breaking it.

One rare summer's afternoon, I asked about the tattoos on his bared arms, and he said: 'These? These are all that's left from my army days, lad.' He threw his cigarette into the street, watched its sparks bounce over the cobbles. He'd been in Australia in the early Sixties, he said. Close to the test ranges.

'Test ranges?'

'Where they exploded the bombs,' he said, running a hand over the rose on his arm. 'The atom bombs, I mean.' It was a fair distance away across the desert, he told me, and they ordered him to turn his back and shut his eyes, so he never saw the flash. There was a wind, though – a wind that blew all over the outback. And when he turned around, the whole earth was climbing into the sky. Afterwards, he heard a black rain had fallen on the people in the desert, but he hadn't seen that. There was no anger in his voice, no judgement.

Young as I was, I understood it was a story he'd told often enough, the same one he listened to every evening inside his silence.

He died soon afterwards, widowing his wife a second time. For some people, there isn't much peace.

It's strange, though. When I remember him now, it isn't the army or the war or atom bombs I think of. It's the flower on his arm. It's the quiet way he explained the fate of the people in the desert.

Stronger Faster Shorter

Our bodies had been destroyed in catastrophic high-speed accidents, then put together again by scientists using bionic technology.

We were stronger now, and faster. We narrowed robotic eyes and zoomed in across vast distances. But the technology had unexpected side-effects. Although we ran faster than speeding locomotives, this had to be expressed in slow motion. So a short sprint-race would consume an entire lunch-hour. And we wasted far too much time in mid-air, slowly completing prodigious leaps.

The most impressive member of our gang was Blakey, who was almost totally bionic. He'd decided to do the whole school-year in slow motion, and consequently was often in trouble with our teachers. Not that he cared. After all, if you've been through the ordeal that Blakey had – every single bone shattered and his body rebuilt, at a cost of six million dollars – then detention is the least of your worries.

I won't pretend it was always easy. Those blessed with massive powers are bound to meet doubters. Henderson, for instance. If I'd been re-engineered, he accused, then how come I was still such a squirt? All that dosh, wouldn't they have made me a foot taller?

Of course, I could have visited the full force of a bulldozer upon his gloating face. Instead, I trained the cross-hairs of my vision on a girl I'd noticed on the other side of the yard.

Dit … dit … dit …

Zooming in, I realised she'd been listening to my conversation with Henderson. Her long brown hair was pulled free from her ear, and she was training it in my direction.

That's when I knew I'd found her, the person I'd been searching for. I waved away Henderson and ignored my silly friends, all of them screwing up their bionic eyes and leaping slowly through the air.

Now I realised they were childish nonsense, the games we'd played. But the strange thing is, as I walked across the yard, I felt the bionics working inside my body. And it sounds daft, I know – but, for the first time in my life, everything moved in slow motion.

Skinner & Dewhurst

'We should bow down before the cows!' he said. 'They've been giving us their milk for yonks, they've let us drink it – we ought to bow down!'

Well, it didn't matter whether you agreed or not, it was embarrassing to hear him say that on the train to college, especially since he meant it, especially as he wasn't taking the piss.

But worse was after we'd got off, when we were taking a shortcut across the field – and I swear that the same train, the exact same train we'd just got off, was stuck there at the signal, with Skinner on his hands and knees in the grass, as good as his word, trying to make us all join him before the cows.

Which Dewhurst did, of course, the idiot.

As for me – well, there were girls watching from that stupid train, all their faces skenning out. So I went off-ski, priming the rest of the class to snigger when they finally wandered in with wet knees. Dewhurst copped the worst of it, because Dewhurst always did.

Dewhurst was still bowing down to the cows weeks later, when Skinner had long since moved on, when he was saluting the peas in Tesco's and chanting *Sieg Heil* to the rusks.

That was Skinner for you: the kid who married his guitar to an amp down by the river, called all dogs Bob, and claimed to have no feeling at all in his knees – and threw himself off a back-alley wall to prove it, then said, 'Felt nowt. Felt almost nowt.'

Dewhurst, high above, stared white-faced into the alley while Skinner yelled, 'On your knees, Dewhurst! On your knees!'

The Inner Peace of Frank Sinatra

Lancashire, 1979

His song, he said, was 'My Way', and he would sing it as the climax of our end-of-year revue. Then we'd know peace, for his voice would carry us skyward.

Some followed his eyes to the heaven he'd promised, but most studied his chest hair, visible through an open-necked shirt, collars sharp enough to have your eye out.

The other Iranian lads hugged him as he strode away, his white jacket blazing through the college's gloomy corridors. It seemed he and his friends had come to our broken town simply to spread their joy through the drizzle.

When the singer instructed us to call him Frank, the conviction burned in his eyes – making me doubt our contribution, a comedy skit that hadn't made anyone laugh during rehearsals.

It was surprising to find him in a flowerbed just before the show. I'd gone outside to conquer my nerves, when I heard him groaning. It took ages to clean his jacket, longer to prise the whisky bottle from his microphone hand.

We dragged him backstage. One of his friends broke down in tears while another poured coffee into him until everyone started laughing and the singer gathered together his jacket's wings, saying 'Frank is ready.'

He fumbled to open the curtain, stumbling slightly as he faced the audience. We watched as he wiped a piece of moss from his lapel. The moss tumbled through the air for an age, long enough for everything else in the auditorium to come down with it.

Then Frank opened his mouth and let out the beauty he had promised.

Afterwards, his friends claimed it had been fated. For only a man who had recovered from ruin could sing that song with such conviction. They went out to the spot where he had fallen, danced in a ring around the flowers, and lifted Frank on their shoulders, high as heaven.

Waiting for Frank's Pigeons

For David Heys

On a Sunday in spring too cold for cricket, with half the world hiding in girl-places, Dave and me tranced in his dad's rickety shed, stopwatch ticking for the working-man's racehorses.

Homers, those pigeons. And they *would* make it across the sea from Belgium, Dave was convinced. But first we needed patience. First we must name nine famous Belgians.

'Your dad couldn't face the wait, eh?' said the neighbour, digging.

Dave nodded, kept our secret in the loft. Frank was down with pigeon-lung, allergic to his own birds.

The afternoon swelled up bigger than a Test Match and we waited, throats tightened by dust and creosote.

'I'd kill to hear cooing,' I told Dave, whose quietened gaze went out through cracks to a sky made of suet.

Magpies, sparrows, a distant kestrel. One grey cloud the size of Afghanistan. I stared at cack, told old anecdotes, tried a bad handstand, said 'guano' in various accents and asked Dave about pterodactyls.

Dave adjusted his Echo & the Bunnymen coat and resisted hitting me, just. He told me about feuds in the pigeon-fancying fraternity, how the baddies razed huts and slipped poison to fledglings or smashed their enemies' chucky-eggs.

I admired Frank's guts, but that shed smelled of Sunday-things we ought to be doing: looking for girls in places they never went; kicking an egg-shaped ball at the substation wall.

Fantastic, the way those pigeons came home! The sudden clamour of wings, a whisper of claws over the hut's tarred roof. Then Dave snagged ropes and lifted flaps, the way his dad had taught him, until the timings had been stamped and the pigeons were free to strut around their coop while we scattered feed and stroked them, thrilled by the invisible paths they had followed.

The Absolute Business

Northern England, 1979

On the last evening of our childhoods, we squeeze onto the front step of my best friend's house and watch the light fade over the street where we've grown up – a few terraced blocks that drip down off the moors towards the cinema where we've watched films together for years: fights on cable cars, endless car-chases disguised as plots, police vehicles going off cliffs. Those are the ones we like, films we rate *spov* and *hooking*, describe at school as *pearling* and *ace*.

The language we've shared, that'll be dead as Latin soon; our little gang will break up. Still, we nail down tactics for staying in touch, name the pubs we'll visit together when our friend returns on leave, using words we don't understand, talking about the Naafi and full-webbing, drinking more than we can believe.

The change has already begun. His hair has been razored to the wood. 'A buzz-cut, this is,' he says. 'The absolute business, lads. Feel it fizz under your fingers.'

We do, and he's right – there's a thrill in that bristle, almost sharp enough to draw blood. But it's his ears that get us, like handles on the side of his head. We've never noticed each other's ears.

'They won't let you in if you're a hippie,' he tells me. 'They want you to be disciplined.'

I nod, and think about that. 'When did you get the idea?' I ask.

'It was a poster,' he says. 'I saw a poster.'

The only posters I ever notice are for films: CARQUAKE, DEATH RACE 2000, GONE IN 60 SECONDS. Sometimes I stop outside the cinema and stare at the glossy images, distantly aware of some other world.

Next time we go, our gang will be smaller. There'll be something missing, something we can all sense. I'll watch the wrecked cars burn, and wonder what it's like to see a real explosion, to feel more than light on your face.

But it's his ears we'll talk about going home – how thin they looked in the evening light. The patient way he let us flick them, there on his front step, on the last evening of our childhoods.

Civil Defence

This happened in the early 1980s just after my aunty's death, when the grown-ups were huddled in the farmhouse, trying to comfort my uncle.

I carried teenage grief in my fists, stamping through the sheep pastures where once I'd played. There was nowhere to put my anger. The beck was unbothered by the stones that bounced off it.

So I kept going, deeper into my childhood, finding the hut where I'd laiked about with cousins. The government owned the hut, and it was off-limits, but we'd always slipped through the wire. Strangers had revved Jeeps there, and shone flashlights. My uncle said it was none of our business. 'Leave them to their war-games. We're nobbut tenants here.'

But we'd found a way of opening the manhole cover beside the hut, and wriggled down the shaft. In the dank vault beneath, we found a row of stiff iron beds, and dozens of boxes containing biscuits. At the time, it had just been weird; but I was eighteen now, and I'd read a few books.

I took aim at the manhole and pelted it with rocks from the beck. It felt good to make little dents in their war-machine.

But then the hatch opened and a white face blazed out. 'What are you playing at?' the face said. 'This is government property.'

The blood rose to my hands. I had one last rock.

'Sod off,' said the face, 'or I'll ring my superiors.'

I nodded in fury. I knew about his superiors. They'd ride out here when the war loomed, to munch on wafers while the radiation poisoned everything.

He shut the lid just as I was taking aim. If he heard my rock strike the hatch, he never returned.

I went back through the fields, heart pounding, eventually giggling at the mad sight it had made, that white face rising from the ground.

But then I saw the farmhouse, its curtains drawn, and the feeling of triumph went out of me. I wiped my feet, and went in.

Butlins With Books

At the university open day, a man with a brown beard kept saying 'module'.

I was put in mind of the Moon.

We sat out on a strip of grass under grey clouds, eating luncheon meat, blinking at the white buildings.

After lunch, *key texts* were displayed in offices made of brick. Everyone started saying 'seminar'. The bright ones flicked their hair.

We stood at the back, watching.

Mum said, 'They're not backward in coming forward.'

In the loo, graffiti on a toilet-roll holder said 'SOCIOLOGY DEGREES – PLEASE TAKE ONE'. On the cubicle, someone had written 'PLAY TOILET TENNIS: SEE OTHER WALL'. Whoever it was, they'd written the same on the opposite side.

I came out dizzy.

The lecturer was checking his watch. We were led to the library, a ship of words.

'Hopefully, you'll be busiest here,' he laughed, nervously.

There was a goth at the back who couldn't keep up, whose metal attachments jangled.

'Of course,' said the lecturer, 'it's not all work work

work,' and he pointed to the roof, where a student gunfight had broken out, with special effects.

'Blimey,' we gasped, as the sheriff toppled out of sight over the side of the building.

Everyone clapped and cheered, except the goth, whose tongue-stud seemed to be giving him stick.

Afterwards, my mum was worried. 'They'll have fallen onto airbags? Surely?'

Then we got in the car and drove back to our world, up the M6.

Heavy

She returns in small things – the light on an apple, the green tint of its skin.

Then it happens. Slowly, I recall the fruit and vegetables she perched on the high freezer, and how she manoeuvred the chopping-board until it was almost out of reach before turning her knife into a blur.

She kept us at arm's length, like her food. Before it seemed possible, she had vanished again with the choppings. We'd feel a rush of air on our necks, then the banging of the door.

These were her rations: broccoli, lettuce, sprouts – everything eaten raw, out of sight.

Her legend grew. We heard she floated at dawn through our block, the Campus Ghost.

Well-wishers came in droves – counsellors and medics, squadrons of Christians bearing guitars. She let them in, sang their hymns. *We plough the fields and scatter ...*

There wasn't much more to her now than her voice. I used to lie on my bed while she sang the hymns, wishing I wasn't so frightened of her. She had swirls of fur on her face, a greenish bruising beneath her skin. Thanks to certain drugs, both cheeks looked like they'd been pumped with air. Her teeth had become too big for her face. She reminded me of a monkey.

In the early hours, there was often a yellow strip of light under her door. Low voices. I would linger in the corridor and try to listen. The effort made my head hurt. Once, I had a dream we were lovers, arm-in-arm by a bonfire in a field. I woke up and played records, trying to figure it out. A lyric planted itself in my head: *Arm yourself because no one here will save you.*

It ended quietly, with none of the drama young people crave. The days were short, the rain thin. I recall coats hanging heavy as trout, wet cagoules folded out from their own pockets. When we came home from our lectures, they had taken her away.

The rest I have to imagine: the way she crept out, leaving her body in the bed – light again, at last.

A Night on the Lash

For Dave Gilliver

Two friends had ventured off the beaten track, but the resort they chose was down on its luck.

They wanted another drink, but, with nightclubs fussy about training-shoes and all the pubs shut, the only option was the chippie.

Standing in a stale doorway, eating handfuls of wet batter, they spotted a sign:

ANNUAL PARTY FOR THE ASSOCIATION
OF PARENTS OF CHILDREN
WITH HAND AND ARM DEFICIENCIES

Beneath that, in smaller type, there was an instruction:

PLEASE KNOCK

So they did, and nothing happened, until a young skinhead with no arms pushed past and hit the door with his skull.

That did the trick. Bouncers appeared. They lifted a little velvet rope and ushered the friends through, into the yeast and smoke of a dingy ballroom, where Eighties hits thudded from the gloom.

On the dance floor a desperate, snarling couple were flailing at each other with their bare hands.

At last, the other dancers yanked them apart.

The woman wept under the strobe lights, bits of hair clinging to her fingers. Her lover was led away to the toilets.

Afterwards, the DJ put on 'Two Tribes'.

The friends took a leathery seat in the corner beside a child. They couldn't work out who the child's parents were, and had become too nervous to enquire, so they concentrated on drinking, hoping that someone would claim her.

Later, the child fell asleep at a stiff angle. She was about seven or eight, they reckoned. Her hands rested in her lap, each with two fingers.

The friends gulped their drinks. After trips to the toilet, they discussed the bloody smear along the urinal. Had it been headbutted? Or punched?

Music thudded. The child slept on, her face smooth and unfussed.

The friends were approached by a man who asked if they knew Barry. When they shook their heads, the man punched his own head in anger. 'Gatecrashers!' he raged. 'At a charity do!'

He made them leave.

Outside, wind thrummed in the promenade's wires. When the friends tried to flag a cab, they noticed their hands. They studied their fingers in the wind.

Smile and Comb Your Hair

I checked their names again. 'Cheese Horn and Wolftoucher?'

Affirmative, they nodded.

The words blared from my notepad. I was the newspaper's cub reporter, I explained, and if I failed to get the organisers' real names, my editor would probably –

'Organisers?' they said. 'We're not the organisers. Snow White, he's the organiser.'

I followed their fingers to a fair-haired man stooped over a console. He was checking the fairy lights and pushed for time, he said. The electrics were his bag, nothing else. The man I wanted was his good buddy Captain Blood. Captain Blood was the brains. It had been his eyeball.

Captain Blood was passing comment on the savouries when I found him. The caterer looked close to tears, and vanished as soon as I announced myself.

'There's a shortage of jelly in these pies,' Captain Blood explained.

How CB Radio hams came to organise the Falklands homecoming, I never discovered – just as I failed to learn Captain Blood's real name. Or 'handle', as he preferred me to call it. Because, just as he was warming up, a truck's hooter sounded.

'Button it,' said Captain Blood. 'Here come the heroes.'

We watched the troops file in, to meet various civic dignitaries and an old boy called Red Rooster who had driven his rig down Hammer Lane before any trucker in the hall.

'It sure is good to see y' all on the flip-flop,' he told the soldiers. 'You followed the stripes home and showed the bucket-mouths where to go! Seventy-thirds, brothers! Two miles of ditch for every mile of road!'

After they'd prised the mic off Red Rooster, I spoke with a Tory councillor who had adopted a strategic position by the sandwiches.

'The closest we'll ever get, eh?' he said in a sad voice, watching the troops.

The one soldier I dared interview was trying to light another cigarette. He didn't recognise me from school, although we'd been in the same class two years previously. Who the hell was Captain Blood, he wanted to know? I shrugged while he steadied his hand.

'Was it bad out there?' I asked him.

'Better than this,' he said.

Malvinas

After they'd rounded the table to poke me with their pool cues and ask what my problem was, I thought it best not to say, letting them tell me, instead, about the Islands, and what they'd endured down there for tossers like me who disturbed a bloke's shot.

And what was I looking at? What was so funny?

Do you like hospital food?

Fancy a knuckle butty?

Want to pick your teeth up with a broken arm?

Or maybe I'd prefer to be shipped home in a body bag, like their mates?

I let it pass, but for years attempted to fashion this reply.

Having been warned that pool cues are clichés, I tried many other sticks in their place:

They rounded the table with a broom …

… with a mop …

There's a political piece featuring flagpoles, and a magic-realist version in which one of the soldiers attacks me with a wand, plus a weirder one where they've somehow got hold of pogo sticks.

In another, the pool cues are rifles and I'm as dead as

the friends they grieve for, the boys who fell at Goose Green.

The War's all around them now: on the next seat in the bus, staring at them across a pub, touching their wives' legs.

No matter where they go, it's there: the power, the shame, the lust, the gift. This pain they must pass on.

Want some, do you? Want some?

The Goat of Mendes

Thinking it would impress Lucifer, the workless slaughter-man slipped fences beyond the allotments and butchered a goat, using his hacksaw to fashion a bedroom altar from the creature's horns, measuring its hot blood into phials.

After his arrest, he blamed amphetamines, said he now conceded that the beast was not the Goat of Mendes but the tender's pet, known by local kids as Fred.

His confession got him bail, but didn't save him. He emerged from court like an animal on the run, to find our pack assembled, our cameras waiting.

No, he couldn't explain it. What else had he known but slaughter?

'My life had fallen apart. You ask how that feels? Here: stitch this.'

When he butted the fella from *The Sun*, I had to swallow my elation, remembering the person I was supposed to be – another cub on the make.

And later I filed my story just like those lads from the tabloids. It wasn't about redundancy or depression, or a way of life falling to bits before our eyes. It was about the Satanist who killed kids' pets.

Ink had never smelled so fresh. I went down to the galleys to watch the compositors turn my words into lead and then wash the lead with ink. It was my first front-page lead, first byline – a trophy I mounted over my bed, until cops forced the door of the bailed man's flat, and cut him down from a flex.

Debut

He introduced himself with a crush of hands.

'Alf Borstal,' he said. 'Manager.'

Told me: 'No fancy stuff. Pump it anywhere, just get it up the pitch. Understand?'

His large German car purred. The other drivers were micks, lesbos, dicks. And many pedestrians were asking for it, too.

Then he called a lamp-post a wanker.

I should have got out right there, right then. *But when you're desperate for a game …*

Besides, I was scared. He had swirls of hair on the backs of his hands, like gas on Saturn. This wasn't a man you argued with. Not a man to entertain doubt.

Maybe it was the hydraulics' whispered threats or the sight of the smashed pavilion, but I foresaw it all before the match even started: a pitch like cat food, Alf's chief tactical weapon a favourable wind, and this bigger mess – not so much the own goal I was fated to score, more the touchline silence that followed, more the miles I ran thereafter in the other direction from the ball, the wind closing my face to a speck.

At full-time, I knew, I would stumble over a bad step into the pavilion to sit beneath another man's trousers, waiting for Alf's analysis of my debut while he put the first-aid bucket in intensive care and pulled the hooks off the wall.

What a Tree Is

In the council meeting, they were debating the plan to include a few saplings in the town-centre redevelopment. Several councillors were worried about the investment, the upkeep. Trees were *potential litter hazards*, they said: imagine the work every autumn!

As a reporter, I'd heard worse. There was a councillor obsessed with *the inner-city grotto*. And another who urged the scrapping of all arts events *when we already have two brass bands each year*.

They tried their best – harder, for sure, than the Press. Our town was down on its luck, and would have been worse without those deliberations on sewers and cracked kerbstones.

But now I didn't care if every sewer in the district collapsed. Although I was pledged to neutrality, I wanted to stand up and defend the saplings.

When I rose, everyone stared in my direction, and I thought: This is it. My chance.

But I traipsed in furious silence from the chamber.

Outside, in reception, I faced a girl with huge brown eyes and hair that went all down her back. As far as I knew, she was the only beautiful woman who had ever entered that building.

Where had she come from? Where was she going?

We didn't speak. She offered a smile which widened her already-enormous eyes, so that they seemed to occupy most of her face.

That was it, nothing more. Outside, I stumbled through the drizzle, counting trees. There were three. We had three trees in our town centre, two bent sycamores and a horse chestnut drooping sorrowfully from its cage.

For a few perfect seconds, I stared up at that horse chestnut, thinking of the girl I had seen. The tree's shape was printed on every leaf, and printed again on every vein, until there was nothing inside it but more tree.

Imagine the work every autumn! Imagine the investment, the upkeep!

I turned and went back towards the council chambers. If the girl was gone, I would burst through the doors and make my speech. I would tell them exactly what a tree was.

Spoons Against Rommel

A stranger has stung me with his yellowed finger in the post-office queue. When I turn around, his cracked eyes stare into mine.

'A little bird tells me tha puts on … *readings*,' he growls.

Gingerly, I nod.

The stranger moves his finger to the sandy brown folds of his coat, from where he digs out two tarnished silver spoons. 'What tha needs,' he says, 'is these weapons. Tha needs these here weapons at thi next poetry do, lad.'

And he clatters the spoons off his elbows. Hips.

'Now, I know what tha's thinking, kidder,' – and I don't doubt it for a second – 'tha's thinking: How's this fella got so good on them damned spoons? Well,' he nods, 'it were in the desert. In the War, in the desert. Sod all to do, and the hours not to do it in. How else is a Tommy to fill his days? Spoons against Rommel!' he declares, and clacks his knees, hands. Face!

'Tha know tha wants it, lad! How about it? Me and these bloody weapons?'

I ponder his spoons. The whole post office ponders his spoons.

He grins. Teeth and holes. Says: 'Grand! That's settled it, cocker. I'll see thee soon.'

But as he waves, his face turns nomadic, wistful. 'Now, then. Think on, lad: book a bit of quality. *Because sometimes even spoons can't save the day.*

'Like this one time when the Saharan war was really dragging,' he remembers, shaking his head slowly. 'Imagine it: I was that bored, I put me spoons away, and dug an hole. Dug an hole and sat in theer. Spoonless. Empty. And dusta know what I thought of, hour on hour? By hell, cocker: cool breezes in Blackpool.

'And I'll tell thee summat else. *Shhh.* Secret. Spoons or no spoons, a fella might wobble in a scrape like that. Aye, he'll turn his share of dirt when he's down a hole in the sand in the desert! Know what I'm saying? Heh?'

And he strides out of the post office, calling: 'Tha'll likely know where to find me. Man alive. What this shop needs. Poetry readings with spoons!'

Theatre Trip During a Storm

For Joe Alessi

The irony of the mud was lost on me until afterwards. Late for a play about the First World War, I'd taken a short cut through a waterlogged field and entered the foyer with filthy shoes.

I muttered apologies to the ushers as I cleaned up, pleased at least not to have missed the start. It was rare for a posh theatre to put on plays set in my old hometown, and even rarer to find a childhood friend playing the lead role, so I decided the wetting was worth it.

But I found it hard to get into the story. The set was built from the wrong kind of bricks. The lead actress never got her accent right. My old friend's commanding performance as a fierce sergeant was undermined by my knowledge that I knew him.

Then came the moment when the womenfolk heard rumours that their husbands had been slaughtered. The storm began to batter so hard on the theatre's roof that the audience lifted their heads, perhaps suspecting a clever sound effect.

The storm's distraction set me on a path back to my childhood. With real rain beating upon a version of my old town, I remembered wandering around our market in the rain. There was a sweet rotting smell that I liked, also a place to drink warm sarsaparilla. And those old women I'd see everywhere, bent women in black clothes, always busy on errands. 'Who *are* they, Mum?' 'Widows,' said Mum, looking into her drink. 'Old widows from the War.'

Later, I thought of other women born to that small town, women who had never found a man at all – without even widowhood's black consolation.

'I shall eat stones,' the character cried when she heard the news about her bloke.

Rain fell harder on the roof, fell like the stones she must eat. I looked up, out of one dream into another – and there was my friend, alive and breathing, at the play's heart.

Children of Dirt and Thunder

Sometimes there's no tale to tell. Sometimes there's just a mountain village and a terrace above a swollen river. Just a cross-eyed woman sweeping up after a storm.

Sure, I could tell you about the crazy taxi-driver and the history of his clutch. Washed-out roads, potholes. The things we saw on the border: people with missing limbs; travellers sitting quietly in the dust, their suits ruined, their shoes worn. Most of them stuck there, but the Western vehicles passing through. And women scrambling to sell the doilies they'd blunted their fingers sewing. A few coins, that's all they wanted. Enough to feed their kids. Mister. Please, mister.

Fighting, you say? Yes, there was fighting nearby. One farmer spoke of depleted uranium in the bomb-casings.

You want to hear about their poverty. We met an astronomer who gave massages to Western sunbathers. A better living, he said – though the Mafia pocketed half his cash, and half the cash of everyone else. The cloakroom assistants, the toilet attendants. These trades, too, required protection.

And, yes, it's true: those goons shouldered their little whores around the hotel and fell on their white bellies into the pool. One of them stroked the kitten he'd balanced on his chest while his teenage servants came and went, carrying rolls of money.

But lie down now. Don't you ever sleep?

This story, it's about an older war, the war that's gone on forever. There are no reporters, no bad guys. Its only bling is cold light. To find it, you leave the border and drive into the mountains, watch lightning lean in for Polaroids.

In a power-cut, on a terrace above a river, that's where you'll find her, an old woman with cross eyes. She'll be mending her vines after the storm, her brush sweeping back the silt where they've hatched, unnoticed, the children of dirt and thunder.

Whatever you want to know, the answer is fireflies. Out of the darkness, they rose like stars to hunt for mates and warn away foes.

You ask me about fighting, and this is the story I tell you. This story about fireflies.

Returned

He comes back after years, parking his car by the alley where cats wail in the small hours. You know him by the *rat-tat-tat* of his knock – the best friend of your dead lover, arriving in a rush, as if the news is fresh, not something you've lived with for ages.

All these years he hardly called – and now this. When his hand touches the door, you wait for a while before opening up, and then stand in silence before him, watching the grief scald his eyes. Barely able to speak, he begs forgiveness until you hold him as you might hold a dying bird, aware of its bones under your fingers, frightened of the pitiful fluttering.

Then you release him, perhaps hoping he's returned with some sign of what this is all about, of the new grief that's brought this old grief back to you.

But he leaves without another word. And you already know, even as his car pulls away, that it'll be years before you see him again, if at all.

What a fate: to stand at the door of a small house and wait, not for the return of your husband, but for the few scraps that remain of him, for those strange moments when old friends are seized by the little things they once failed to do …

Comforts of a kind, like the cat running its silk round your legs, proof that we all take a while to truly die, that we don't vanish completely until everyone who remembers us is gone.

That's what you'd like to think, anyway, as you watch the tail-lights of your visitor's car, and the car goes round the corner that you once thought of as *ours*.

Ours for a while longer yet – for a few more years.

Oh God, that more grief would come to your door, that they'd bring it each night, a line of cats laying their bloody gifts on your step.

Journey of the Burned Man

As the bulky middle-aged man struggles with change for the bus driver, I study the burns on the back of his head.

Immediately, he's greeted by a thick Mancunian voice: 'Sean! Sean, my friend!' The man who hails him is about the same age and weight, his hair likewise razored to the bone. The greeting is so cheerful I wonder whether it contains mockery.

'Hallo, Christopher,' says Sean, sitting down five seats in front, not bothering to glance back.

'Nice to see you, Sean.'

'You too,' Sean tells the floor of the bus.

From my position between the two men, I have a view of Sean's injuries, an island-chain of burns stretching over face, scalp and neck. They carry me back to my job in prison, where sex offenders suffered attacks from inmates wielding kettles.

'Talk to me,' says the voice, softer now. 'It's Christopher, remember.'

'I'm not ignoring you,' says Sean coolly. 'But this is a public place, Christopher. We can't talk here.'

'Don't be like that, Sean. Where have you been?'

'To church,' Sean replies. 'I got my tie cleaned too.'

Stiffly, without looking back, he holds up a long, thin plastic bag.

'Me, I went to the cathedral,' says the voice.

'Good. You're a lovely man,' replies Sean, in the same cool tone.

'So are you, Sean. What time do you have to be back?'

'Half-twelve. You?'

'They want me in later.'

Sean smooths his tie. 'This is my stop. So long, Christopher. Watch yourself, now.'

'You too,' says Christopher, his voice quiet.

I watch Sean get off. He waddles to a hectic crossroads and sits on a bench, stroking the dry-cleaning bag.

When the bus goes by, Christopher waves, but Sean keeps his eyes fixed on the bag. His scalds look worse in daylight, more pink and raw. The sugar must have stuck to his skin.

Blackbirds are busy in the hedgerows. Overhead, jets climb away from the city. Far below, a scarred churchgoer sits by the roadside, tracing the contours of his dry cleaning.

How smooth it looks, his favourite tie. How clean and unspoiled.

Tor

Each morning I went down into their silence, into an agony of tea-spoons, various rituals with marmalade and knives.

Whatever grief had befallen the couple, they had brought it to the hotel. Their bodies were stiffened by it, their eyes made lifeless and grey. Although it made me tense to watch them, I came to track their joyless wanderings, noticing mud on their boots when they returned, threads of corn that wouldn't come loose from their cardigans. I thought of them whenever I wandered Glastonbury's lanes.

At the last breakfast, they blessed me with shocking smiles.

It had happened, the woman said, her eyes brightening – they had felt it on the Tor, a humming, a sense of enormity.

In the grass, her husband added. When we lay together in the grass.

That early in the day, I was unsure how to respond. They weren't like the town's hippies. Their shoes were sensible, their hair tidy and grey. You could imagine them sitting under tartan blankets, waiting for a gas stove to boil.

The man said: There are forces we can't ignore.

His voice was loud enough to silence the other guests. I stood before him, smiling stupidly.

Forces, said the woman. Ancient forces, at work on the Tor.

She was pinched and alert by her husband's side. The man wiped his glasses with a cloth, nodding vigorously. Of course, the military *know*, he said. They want us gone.

Now his wife was also nodding. But we won't go, she said. Not now.

Not now it's been revealed, said her husband.

Later, when it began to rain, I saw them romp past the window as they set off up the Tor. I didn't like the desperation in their joy. It struck me as less human than the quiet dignity of their grief.

The Balloonist's Tale

My first training flight, Bob guided us to the middle of nowhere, then pretended to have a heart attack. I'd no idea what was happening until I heard him laughing, the daft sod.

He didn't talk much, Bob. Didn't need to, I guess. Apart from laughs, it was the silence we liked, the moments after you'd burned some gas and were drifting, looking down on the trees.

One summer evening, we went to the county's south. Lush fields. Orchards and such-like. Just a dog barking.

Bring her down, said Bob.

The balloon was always a lady to Bob.

Here? I said, because I didn't like the look of those tight fields.

A new trick, winked Bob. And slowly I brought her down, following his instructions.

Caravans, I pointed.

They certainly are.

We can't land there, Bob.

He smiled mysteriously. Just a flying visit, he said.

Below, folk were coming out to look. As we descended, I started to see a lot of blonde hair.

Girls, Bob! All of them!

He nodded. Lithuanians, he said. Fruit-pickers.

Down, we sank, into that orchard of women.

About fifty feet above the field, Bob took the controls and pulled off a daring sweep. Then he produced a red rose from somewhere and let it fall through the air.

The lass who caught it was lithe and tall. She didn't have to grab for it; the flower just fell into her possession. Her face gleamed up at us like an apple in the sunshine. As she sent back a kiss, Bob hit the gas and the balloon rose away.

Soon the Lithuanian girls were far below and the hills had drawn their cloaks around them.

You knew those girls?

Bob set his gaze on the meadows. Just one of them, he replied.

Later, when it came time to land, I pushed too hard.

Gently now, he said.

We came down in a patch of sunlight, the smoothest landing I'd managed. Then we folded the balloon into the basket and waited for the pick-up, taking turns at a beer.

We lay back and pointed at the places we'd been, the tracks we'd followed through the sky.

The Good Times

She dumped him over the phone, during a thunderstorm. He listened calmly as she explained. They were incompatible, she said. Emotionally, she said.

Physically, he thought.

We're on different wavelengths, she said.

You're too beautiful, he thought.

Halfway through the meandering, undramatic exchange, his fatalism seemed to exasperate her and he wondered whether the call was her attempt to rouse him, to seek some of the strength she appeared to crave.

This could be the moment, he thought.

There was a thunderclap from down the line. They lived in towns separated by a few miles of uninspiring fields, and the sound-wave took a few seconds to travel from her town to his.

Thunder, he said. The same thunder. I heard it twice.

Her sigh encouraged him. It sounded fond. But he didn't know whether she was sighing about his enthusiasm for thunder or sighing because he could not be saved.

The conversation meandered to its close. By then, she had apologised for breaking up with him and he had accepted her decision.

It isn't easy for the beautiful; he had sympathy for

their plight. He stared out over the fields beyond his house, where rain fell on the pylons. He followed the wires into the distance, wishing that he felt angry, searching for a gesture of rage.

Then he thought: If I'm weak, if I'm passive – that's OK. There are other fates. I could be cruel, that would be worse.

He listened to the purr of the rain, steady and gentle as the flame on a stove. He was hungry now, he realised, and cold. Later, after he'd eaten, he would run a bath.

He stared at the streaky window, hoping it would rain all day. He wanted the comfort of dark skies and a bubbling gas-fire. If these were the bad times, he'd try to enjoy them. There was nothing to prove now, no one beautiful to convince, or to live up to.

Slowly, the storm passed over his town, just as it had passed over hers. He lay on his bed trying to imagine the lives that lay before it, the lovers it would rain upon.

Acknowledgements

Thanks to the following people for encouraging me to fire off these flashes: Peter Blair and Ashley Chantler, wise stewards of *Flash: The International Short-Short Story Magazine*, in which all the stories except the title story were first published; The Owls of Athens (Ed Hogan, Bethan Roberts, and Karen Stevens); Frances Everitt and Jon Wyatt (Bridport Prize); Tim Lay and Amy Zamarripa (Grit Lit, Brighton); Simon Jenner, Alan Morrison, and John O'Donoghue (Waterloo Press, Hove); Andre Mangeot and Trish Harewood (CB1, Cambridge); and Lancaster Litfest. I am grateful to colleagues in the Department of English and Creative Writing at the University of Chichester. Individuals and organizations who have helped over the years, even if they didn't know it, include: Linda Anderson; Pete Barnes; Kerrith Bell; Kate Betts; Manuelito Biag; Alan Burns; Jonathan Carr; David Craig; Hugh Dunkerley; Clare Dunne; James Ebdon; Martin Elvins; Simon Finch; Naomi Foyle; David Gilliver; Steve Haywood; Tom Hazuka; W. N. Herbert; David Hesmondhalgh; Julia Hesmondhalgh and Ian Kershaw; Rachel Hughes; Chris Jones; Mimi Khalvati; Jemma Kennedy; Jeannette Laouadi; Zak Malkinson; Ian Marchant; Tom Melk and Sarah Potter; Kai Merriott; Anke Mittelberg; Natalia de la Ossa; Roger Rees; Johnny Rowley; Henry Shukman; Jan Willem Sligting; Helen Steward; Geoff, Jennie, Steven, and Joanne Swann; Lorna Thorpe; Truus, Ellen, Karin, and Mirjam Vermond; Stewart Wills; and the editors of *Staple*, *Zembla*, *Texts' Bones*, and Spitfire Press. I'd like to thank the scientist who described his life's work as 'leaping from failure to failure with undiminished enthusiasm'. And all Germans for their word *Verschlimmbesserung* – 'an intended improvement that only makes things worse'. Last word for Angela Vermond, who makes things better.